DESPICABLE ME

MINION MADE ™

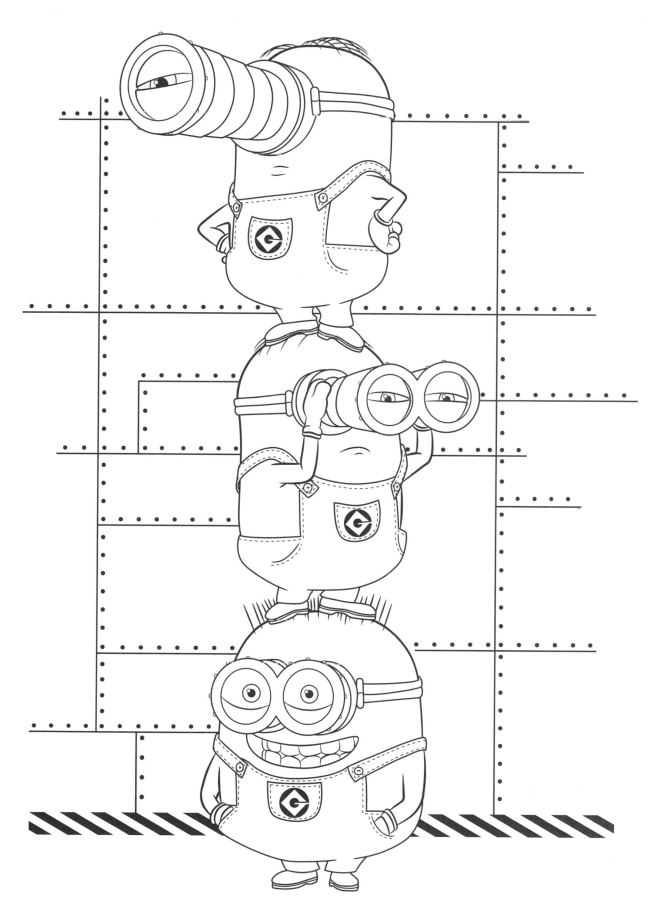

Caution: Minions at work!

All in favour, say "eye!"

You say Poopaye! I say Bello!

It's good to be a Minion!

How many words can you make using the letters in:

DESPICABLE ME

_____   _____

_____   _____

_____   _____

_____

_____

_____

_____

_____

_____

_____

_____

One in a Minion!

It takes a villain to catch a villain.

Team Minion

Why is Gru recruited by the Anti-Villain League?
Use the code to find out.

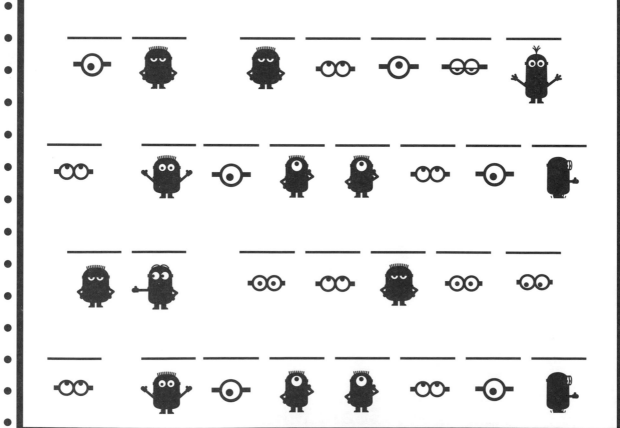

Just a friendly Bello!

I'm so bad, I'm good.

Minions need love, too.

The Magnificent Minions

How many Minions do you count?

Your Answer:

So many Minions, so little time!

One is never enough!

Minions rock!

Quiet please – test in progress.

Which leads to the sundae with a cherry on top?

Answer:

Go bad or go home.

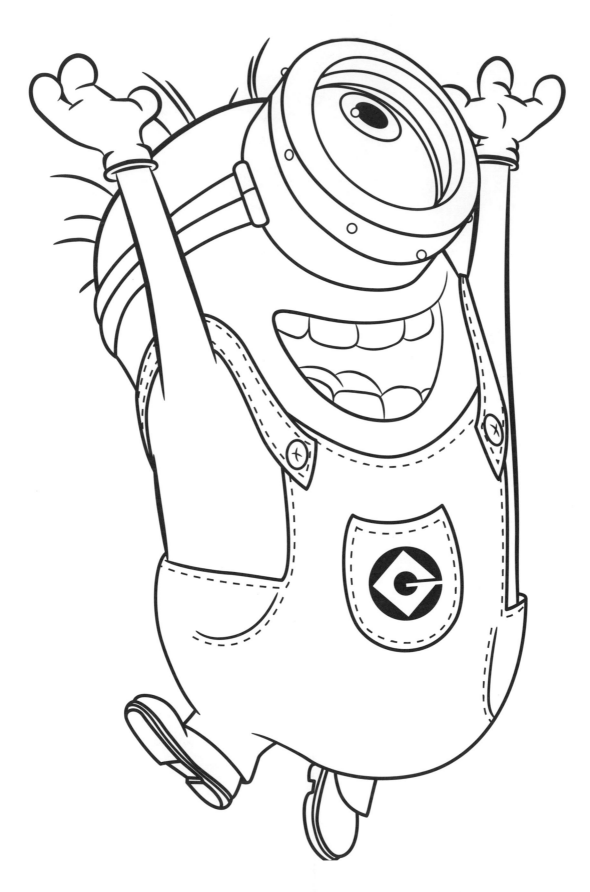

Little Minion, lots of mischief.

99% Adorable, 1% Despicable

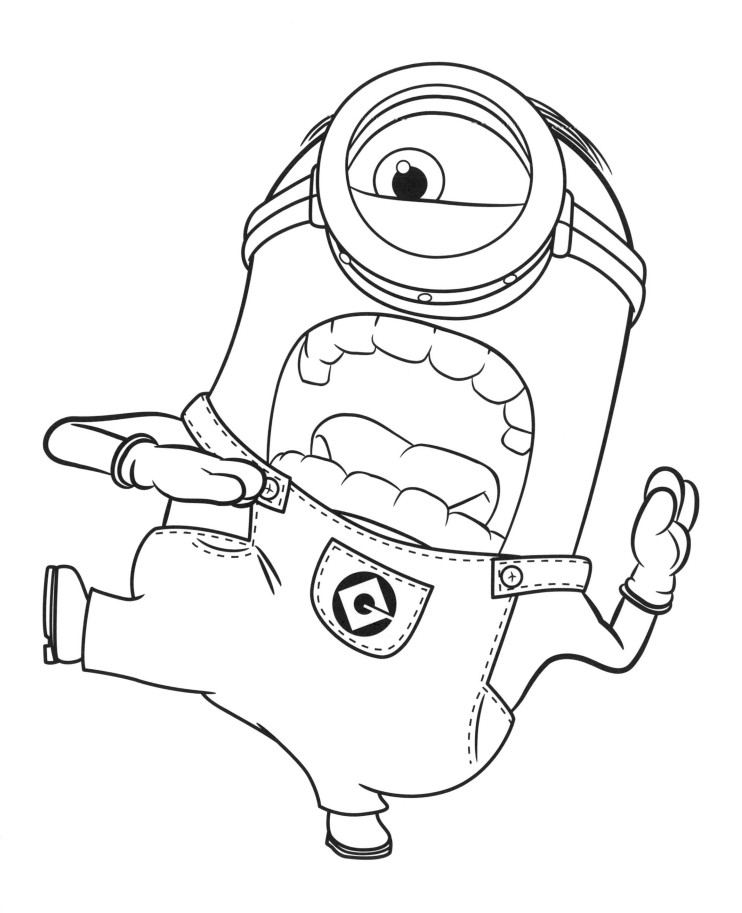

Minion Powered

Match the Minion to the correct shadow.

Answer : D

I don't share.

It's so hard to be good.

**It's all fun and games until
someone loses an eye.**

Look up, down, across, and diagonally. Help the Minions find these despicable words!

MINION
BELLO
POOPAYE
KARATE
BANANA

```
M P J I N G T H E T N
L O Q K A R U P S N O
U O C B A N A N A Q I
K P A E D R O G T I N
J A T L O T A O C G I
Z Y N L K R L T K J M
H E T O C B D U E G P
```

Yellow is no longer mellow.

I <3 Gru

Which pieces complete the picture?

A

B

C

D

E

Family First

Gru: 1 World: 0

A Minion in shining armour.

>:p

You say Goodbye and I say Yellow.

You say Despicable like it's a bad thing.

It's a wild ride!

Let's hula!

**Use the grid
to draw Tom.**

Proud to be a Minion

Uh-oh. . .

There's a new Gru in town!